Exploring the Psalms

A Creative Colouring Journal

By Jacqui Grace

Published in the United Kingdom in 2020 by
Just Cards Publishing
A division of Just Cards Direct Limited
Unit 5 Hallcroft Trade Centre, Hallcroft Road, Retford, Nottinghamshire, DN22 7SS.

ISBN: 978-0-9934231-4-7

A CIP catalogue record for this book is available from the British Library.

Graphic design by Emily Lee
Printed by GPS Printing Ltd, Slovenia

This book can be ordered from any good bookshop or direct from the publisher on their trading website justcardsdirect.com

For more information about Just Cards Publishing and their publications see justcardspublishing.com

CONTENTS

The book of Psalms provides the perfect setting for a colouring journal. Not only is it full of vivid picture language and colourful descriptions, but it also honestly depicts the highs and lows of life. The writers don't gloss over hard questions, difficult and confusing situations and the very real struggles and temptations of life. Yet, alongside all of that, there are outpourings of praise and worship accompanied by an unshakable trust in a faithful God who sees, knows and cares.

I have chosen ten Psalms to delve into. Each Psalm follows a similar pattern:

1. A verse to colour

Before you begin the colouring page, take a little time to pray that God will meet with you as you colour and enjoy being creative. Think about the words you are colouring and try to commit them to memory. Maybe you could look up the verses in a Bible and read the whole Psalm. Most importantly, relax, slow down and enjoy the process!

2. A place to journal

These pages explore the verse or theme in a little more depth. There is space for you to write, doodle and draw as you respond to the words of Scripture. You might want to do this quietly on your own, or meet up with a friend and work through it together, sharing your thoughts and prayers with each other.

3. A moment to "be still"

The phrase "Selah" is often used in the Psalms and is translated as "to pause, stop and breathe". Instead of rushing on to the next thing, take a little time to simply rest

and consider what God is saying to you. Sometimes there is a pattern to colour to help you do this, or a space for you to make notes or drawings. Sometimes I have suggested a creative project. As you do these activities, take your time and continue listening to God.

You will need...

- A Bible.
- A selection of pens, pencils and pencil crayons. If you are using felt-tipped pens, it's a good idea to test them in a small area first to make sure that they don't bleed through the page.
- A pencil sharpener and eraser.

You don't have to start at the beginning; there may be a particular Psalm or theme that stands out to you, and if so, begin there. The most important thing is that you make this little book your own. Fill it with your thoughts, questions and prayers. Enjoy being creative and delight in the process of adding colour and beauty to the illustrations.

I pray that as you complete the pages of this journal you will meet with God in a new and fresh way, and that as you *"draw near to God, he will draw near to you"*. *James 4v8 (ESV)*

Jacqui Grace

Psalm 100
Enter his gates with thanksgiving; go into his courts with praise. Give thanks to him and praise his name. For the LORD is good, His unfailing love continues forever.
Psalm 100 v 4-5 (NLT)

ENTER HIS GATES WITH
thanksgiving

Worship and thankfulness are like a key that opens the way into God's presence.
a thankful HEART
Fill the hearts with things you are thankful for.

THANKFULNESS
CHALLENGE....
Why not make this an everyday habit?
Buy an old calendar or diary and aim to
fill everyday with thankfulness!

You will need...

- Coloured felt
- Photocopied template
- Needles and pins
- Embroidery thread
- Scissors
- Ribbon or string
- Cotton wool/stuffing
- Star sequins (optional)

Instructions

Using the photocopiable template, cut two heart shapes from your coloured felt

If you are adding stars or other decorations to your heart, do this before moving on to the next step.

Pin the two felt hearts together with the outside facing outwards. Tuck your hanging ribbon between the two layers and pin in place.

Sew small running stitches all the way around the edge of your heart, leaving a gap for stuffing. Gently poke a small amount of stuffing or cotton wool inside your heart, then close up the gap with more running stitches.

Why not add some small star sequins to your heart as a reminder that God's love reaches to the heavens
(Psalm 103 v11 and Psalm 36 v5)

Photocopiable template
Print onto paper, cut out the heart shape and pin to your felt.

Gap for stuffing

Thankful

Psalm 84
How lovely is your
dwelling place,
O Lord of hosts!
Even the sparrow finds a home,
and the swallow a nest for herself,
where she may lay her young,
at your altars, O LORD of hosts,
my King and my God.
Blessed are those who
dwell in your house,
ever singing your praise!
Psalm 84 v 1,3 and 4 (ESV)

even the sparrow has found a home

Psalm 84 v 3

make yourself at home!
Blessed are those who dwell in your house.
Psalm 84 v4
Spend some time "dwelling" (in other words resting, staying and lingering) in God's presence. Imagine curling up in a huge, comfortable chair and relaxing in His protection and care.
What would you like to say to Him?

MY SOUL THIRSTS
for the
LIVING GOD
PSALM 42 V2

Do you ever feel worn out and weary, or maybe dissatisfied and longing for more? The psalmist compares this yearning to a thirst. Read Psalm 42 v1-2, and Psalm 63 v 1-8. Can you identify with anything from these verses?

revive
SATISFY
rest
REFRESH
QUENCH
soak
DRENCH
restore
life
SATURATE
fulfil
flood
drink
What promises can you find in John4 v13-14, Isaiah 41v17-18 and Matthew 11v28?
OVERFLOWING

Psalm 37...

Trust in the LORD,
and do good; dwell in the land
and befriend faithfulness. Delight
yourself in the LORD and he will give
you the desires of your heart. Commit
your way to the LORD; trust in him and
he will act... Be still before the LORD
and wait patiently for him.

Psalm 37v3-5 and 7 (ESV)

Be
STILL
before the
LORD
and wait
PATIENTLY
for
HIM

Read Psalm 37 v3-7

(try looking it up in a few different Bible versions)

Make a list of all the verbs/actions listed in these verses.

Which of these do you find the most challenging?

Further reading...
look at John 15v9
(and Proverbs 3v5-6)

Choose one word that is particularly significant for you at the moment and write it in the banner. Spend some time thinking and praying about what this word means to you. (if it's helpful you could add drawings and doodles!)
My Prayer...

Psalm 103
For as high as the heavens are above the earth, so great is his steadfast love towards those who fear him; as far as the east is from the west, so far does he remove our transgressions from us.
Psalm 103 v11-12 (ESV)

as
HIGH
As the
Heavens
are
above the
Earth,
so great is HIS LOVE

Have you ever wondered how much God loves you?

Look at Psalm 103v11-17. The answer is that He loves us more than we can imagine or measure.

- *East and west never meet (v12)*
- *Space is infinite (V11)*
- *Everlasting never ends (v17)*

He loves and forgives us without limit and without end.

What does it mean to you to know that you are loved with an unconditional and immeasurable love?

Read Ephesians 3 v 14-21

Can you make this your prayer too?

How broad and long and high and deep is Christ's love ...

THE ONE WHO WATCHES OVER
YOU WILL NOT SLUMBER...
THE LORD KEEPS WATCH
OVER YOU AS YOU COME AND GO,
BOTH NOW AND FOREVER.

Psalm 121v 3 and 8 (NLT)

The LORD
WILL WATCH
over YOUR
COMING
and
GOING
both NOW
and forever more.

Verse 4 of Psalm 121 says that God does not slumber or sleep. There's never a moment when He's not watching over you, never a moment when He's too distracted or too tired. He's there for you always, all day, all night. Always.

Think about your plans for today or maybe the next few days. What are you doing? *Where are you going? Who are you meeting? Is there anything you are dreading? Or anything you are really looking forward to? Whatever your day holds, remember that God is with you.*

Psalm 139

Read Psalm 139 v 1-18 in a couple of different translations, making a note of any words or phrases that stand out to you.

If I rise on the wings of the dawn, if I settle on the far side of the sea, even there your hand will guide me. Psalm 139 v9-10 (NIV)

ALWAYS

Psalm 23
The Lord is my shepherd;
I shall not want.
He makes me lie down in green pastures.
He leads me beside still waters.
He restores my soul.
He leads me in paths of righteousness
for his name's sake.
Even though I walk through the
valley of the shadow of death,
I will fear no evil, for you are with me;
your rod and your staff,
they comfort me.
Psalm 23:1-4 (ESV)

the LORD is my shepherd

You are WITH me
Psalm 23 v4
Psalm 23:4 says..
"Even though I walk through the valley... you are with me"
Jesus, the good shepherd, will never leave us or abandon us. He promises to walk WITH us however hard, painful or confusing our circumstances may be.
Even though...
...I know you are with me!

The Bible is full of similar promises. Have a look at Isaiah 43:1-2, Romans 8:38-39 & Joshua 1:9
Maybe there is another special verse you hold onto when things are tough?
Choose a verse and then write the words in between the waves

make your own pattern...

I waited patiently for the LORD;
He turned to me and heard my cry.
He lifted me out of the slimy pit,
out of the mud and mire;
He set my feet on a rock and
gave me a firm place to stand.
He put a new song in my mouth,
a hymn of praise to our God.

Psalm 40 v1-3 (NIV)

He hears my CRY
Psalm 40 v1

God Hears You!

What is the cry of your heart? Maybe it's for breakthrough in a difficult situation, a prayer you've been longing to see answered, or a hope for a future that seems uncertain... whatever it is, you can be sure that God hears your cry.

What are some of the things about God that you know to be true, rock solid and unchangeable? Begin to fill the rocks with some of these words.

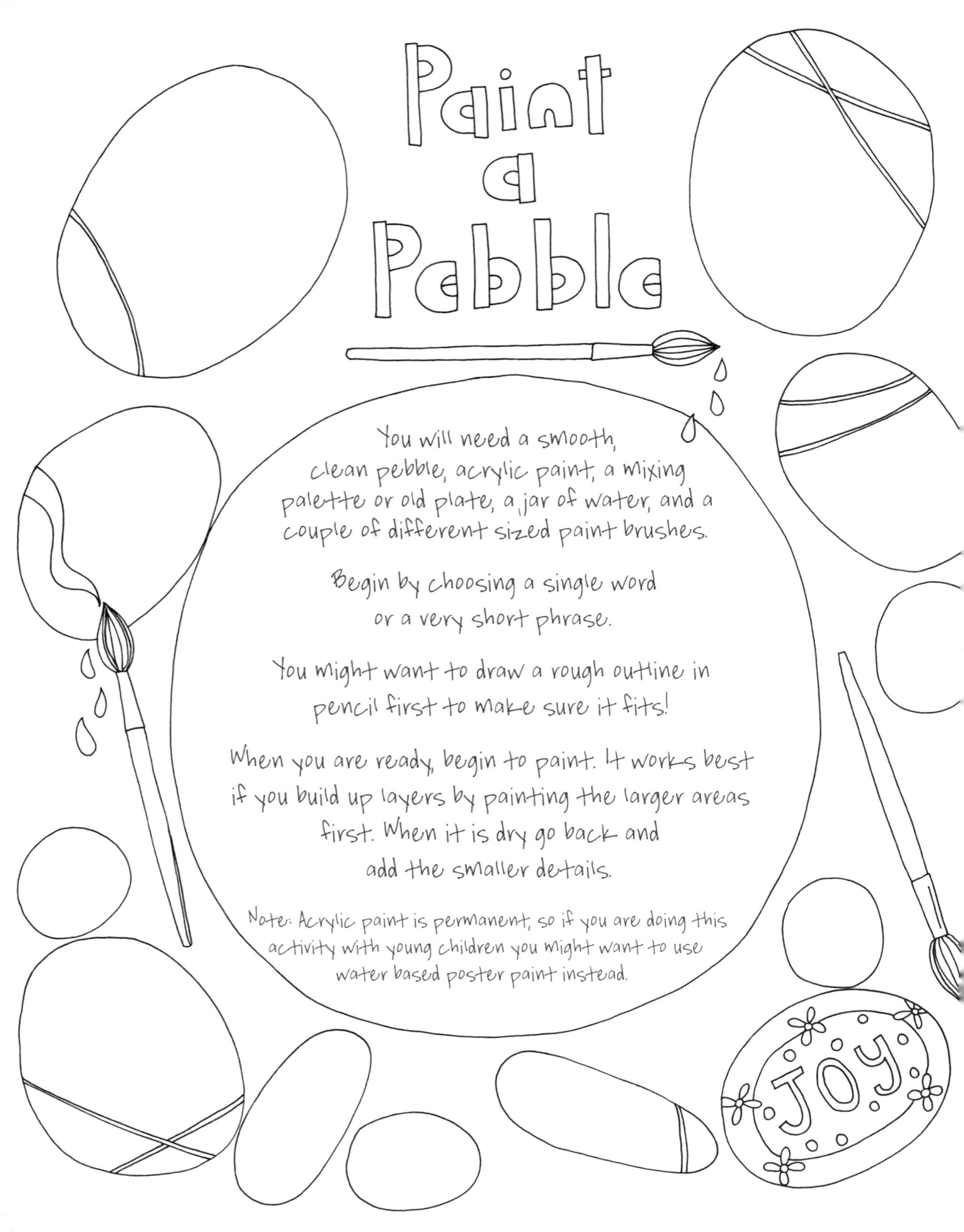
Paint a Pebble
You will need a smooth, clean pebble, acrylic paint, a mixing palette or old plate, a jar of water, and a couple of different sized paint brushes.
Begin by choosing a single word or a very short phrase.
You might want to draw a rough outline in pencil first to make sure it fits!
When you are ready, begin to paint. It works best if you build up layers by painting the larger areas first. When it is dry go back and add the smaller details.
Note: Acrylic paint is permanent, so if you are doing this activity with young children you might want to use water based poster paint instead.
JOY

. design your own.

I will say of the LORD, "HE is my refuge and my fortress, my God in whom I trust. Truly he is my rock and my salvation; he is my fortress, I will never be shaken."

Psalm 91v2 and Psalm 62v2 (NIV)

He is my
REFUGE
and
MY
FORTRESS.
MY
GOD
in whom I
TRUST

FEATHERS AND FORTRESSES

Psalm 91 gives two quite different pictures of the way that God protects and cares for us. From the power, strength and solidness of a fortress, to the soft, tender protection and gentleness of a bird's wings (see v2 and v4).

Which of these examples do you identify with most? Why?

"He will cover you with his feathers, and under his wings you will find refuge."
Ps 91v4 (NIV)

My Refuge & Shelter

Where (or who) do you run to for safety and help?

Choose a verse to write inside the castle.

WORD ART

What images spring into your mind when you think about the word 'DWELL'?

Maybe, you see it like a tree putting down roots?

Or perhaps it's more like building something lasting and permanent?

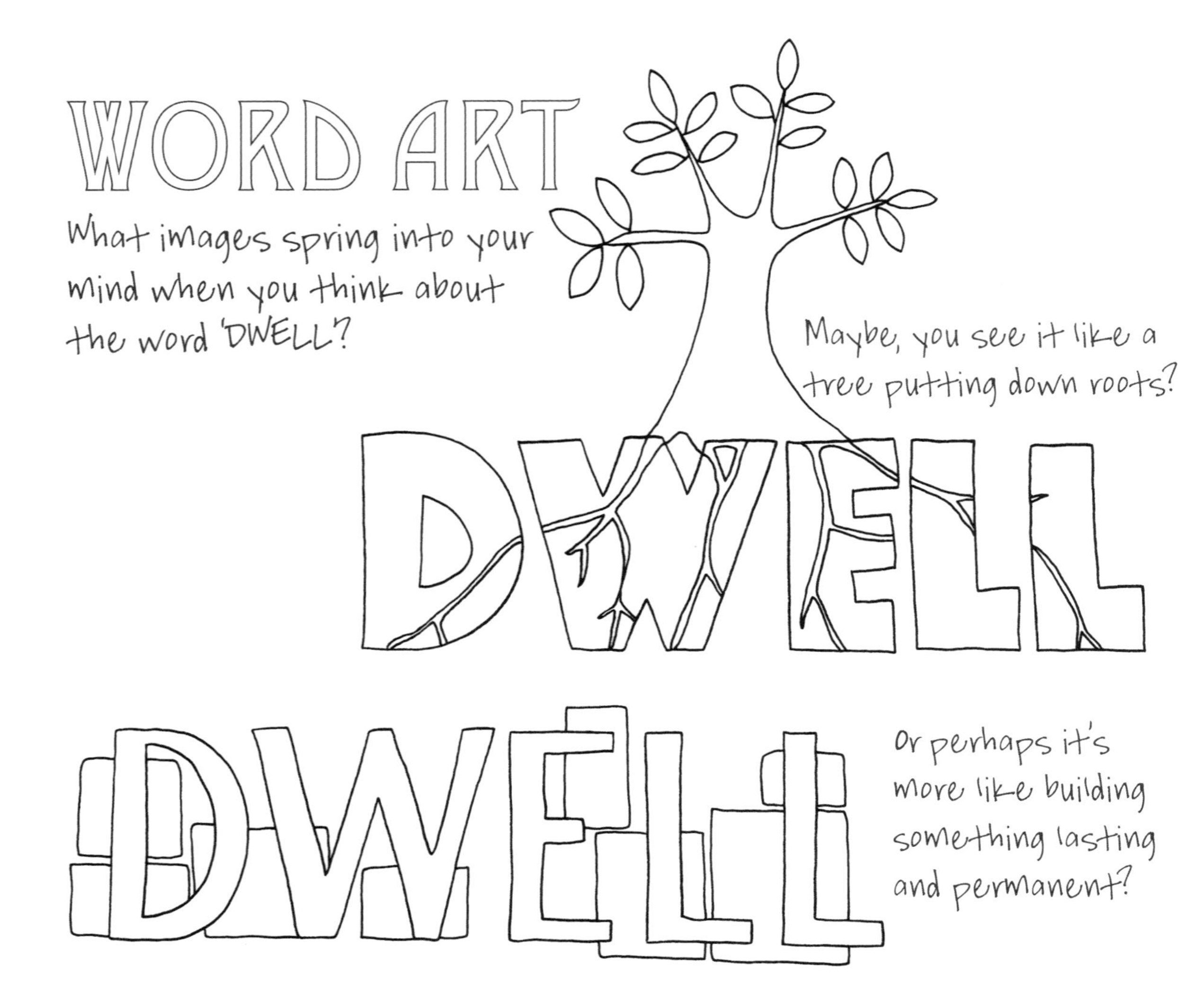

Spend some time thinking about the word 'dwell'. You might want to read Psalm 84 and Psalm 91 again and then begin to decorate the word below.

DWELL

Why not use the next page to create your own word art or alternatively reflect on what God might be saying to you?

Psalm 71
For
you have been
my hope, Sovereign
Lord, my confidence
since my youth... and to
this day I declare your
marvelous deeds.
Psalm 71v5 and 17 (NIV)

AND TO this DAY
I STILL
PROCLAIM
YOUR
WONDROUS
Deeds

in EVERY SEASON

All my life you have been faithful....

Before you formed me in the womb you knew me. (Jeremiah 1v5)

From my youth you have taught me. (Psalm 71v17)

Even to my old age and grey hair you will sustain me. (Isaiah 46v4)

All my life I will praise God. (Psalm 146v2)

In Psalm 71, the writer can look back on his life and see that God has been faithful to him. Use the timeline below to think about some of the significant times in your life when you have been aware of God's faithfulness and goodness (You might want to continue on a separate piece of paper)

Faithful

Bible Study
What are the key themes?
my Questions
What am I reading?
What do I want to remember?
What is GOD saying?
Date:
my prayer...
What do I need to do?

Weekly PRAYER DIARY

today I'm praying for...

Monday

Tuesday

Wednesday

Thursday

Friday

Saturday

Sunday

answers to
prayer...

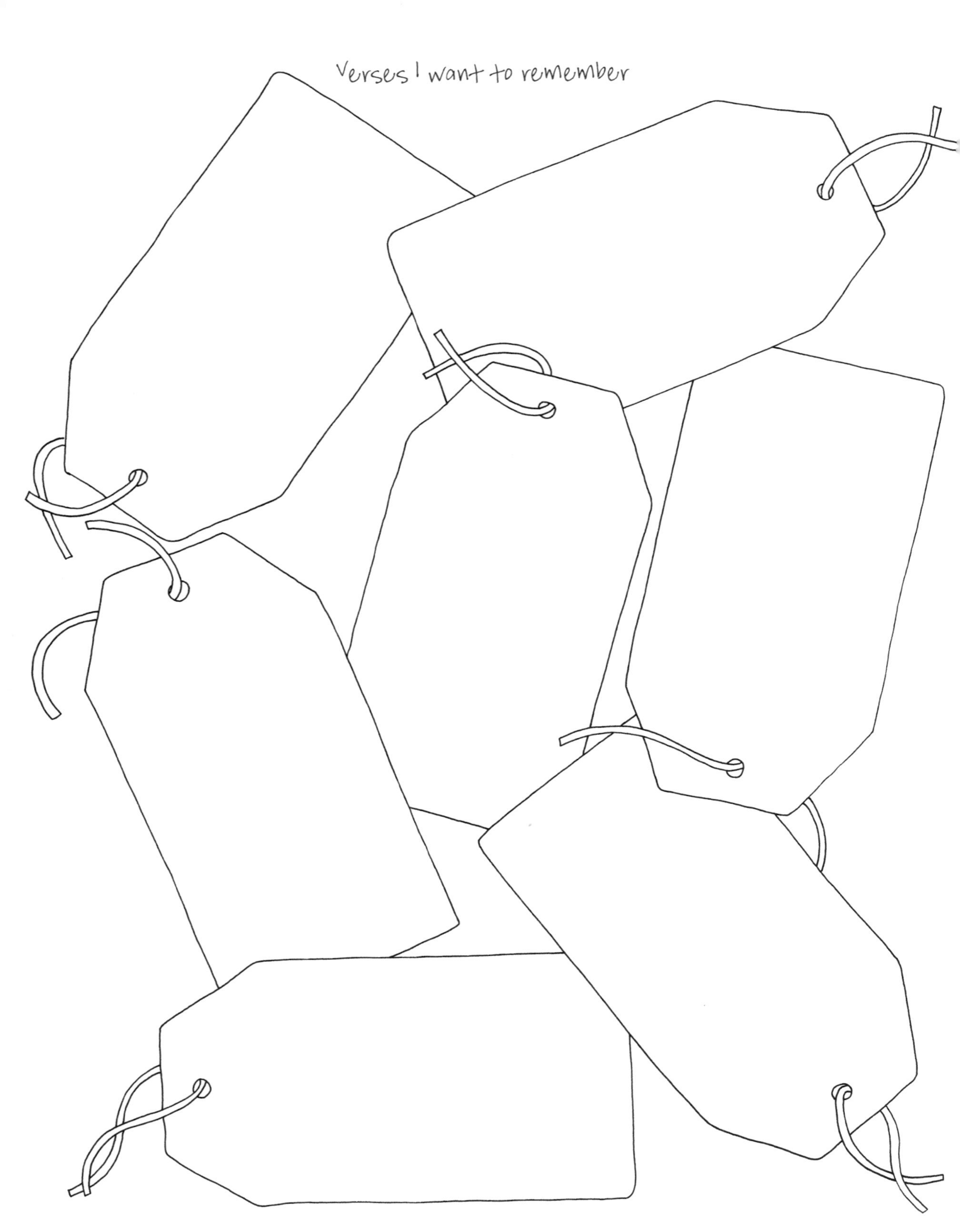
Verses I want to remember

Your word is a lamp to my feet
and a light to my path.

Psalm 119:105 (ESV)